EXTREME DOT TO DOT

LEGENDS & LORE

MindWare
brainy toys for kids of all ages®

www.mindware.com

A MindWare® Original!

Our entire selection of Brainy Toys for Kids of All Ages® is available at www.mindware.com, or by calling us at 800-999-0398 to request a catalog.

Coloring Books

Each of our coloring books offers one-of-a-kind patterns, textures and styles you make your own by choosing how to bring them to life.

Animal Habitats Series

Creature Camouflage Series

Designs Series

Illuminations Series

Lights Series

Modern Patterns Series

Mosaics Series

Quilts Series

Scapes Series

Transformations Series

Puzzle Books

Our puzzle books build skills in many areas—from logic to math, spatial reasoning to verbal skills.

Analogy Challenges

Analogy Crosswords

Clip Clue Puzzles

Code Breakers

Coin Clues

Deducibles

Directive Detective

Extreme Dot to Dot

Fast Facts Trivia

Grid Perplexors

Letter Links

Logic Links

Math Mosaics Series

Math Path Puzzles

Math Perplexors

Noodlers

Number Circuits

Number Junctions

Perplexors

Sequencers

Tactic Twisters

Tan-Tastic Tangrams

Venn Perplexors

Word Winks

Word Wise

Wordoku Puzzles

Games and Activities

Building blocks to strategic games, mystery puzzles to imaginative play — enhance abstract thinking and reasoning skills with our ingenious games and activities.

Bella's Mystery Decks

Blik-Blok

Block Buddies

Chaos

Cross-Eyed

CrossWise

Dizios

Flip 4

Gambit

Guacamole

Hue Knew?

Hue Knew? On the Go!

Loose Change

Logic Links Game

Make Your Own Mask Kit

Noodlers Game

Pattern Play

Q-bitz

Qwirkle

Qwirkle Cubes

Squzzle Puzzles

Talk In Text

Tally Rally

Up for Grabs!

Zenith

© 2010 MindWare Holdings, Inc.

Illustrations/Puzzles by Adam Turner

ISBN 978-1-936300-02-0
SKU 48153

for other MindWare products visit
www.mindware.com

What does it take to become a legend?

Bravery? Magic? The ability to breathe fire? When you venture into the mysteries of ancient legends and folklore, there is no telling what you will discover. The puzzles in this book are no exception. As you make your way through hundreds—sometimes thousands—of dots, the object of your quest is unknown. But once you complete the puzzles, you will have traveled to a sunken city, spied a hidden treasure and looked a monster in the eye. With up to 1,400 dots, these puzzles themselves will become legendary!

The largest puzzles feature crafty clues to get you thinking and each solution is accompanied by fascinating facts. In addition to learning about the legends, you will also build fine-motor skills, strengthen mapping skills and improve concentration—all while enjoying hours of fun!

Instructions

Starting with dot number 1, connect the dots in numeric order. If a number is next to a circle rather than a dot, pick up your pencil and search for the next consecutive number. This number may be anywhere within the design; it may not be near where you left off. Continue in this manner, picking up your pencil whenever you reach a circle until you have connected the last dot. Solutions are provided at the back of the book.

Ready for more?

Check out other MindWare Extreme Dot to Dot titles:

Animals

Explorers

Prehistoric

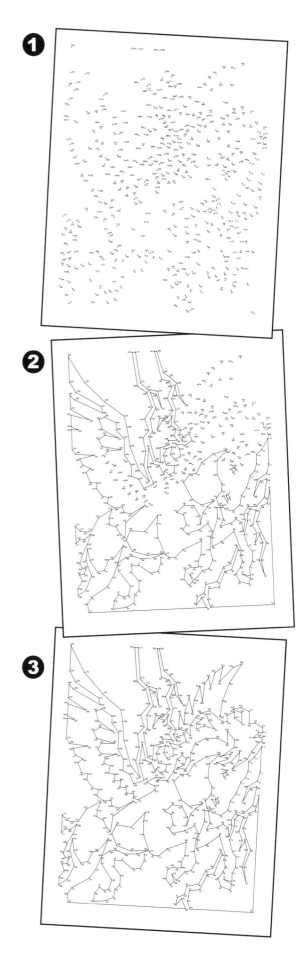

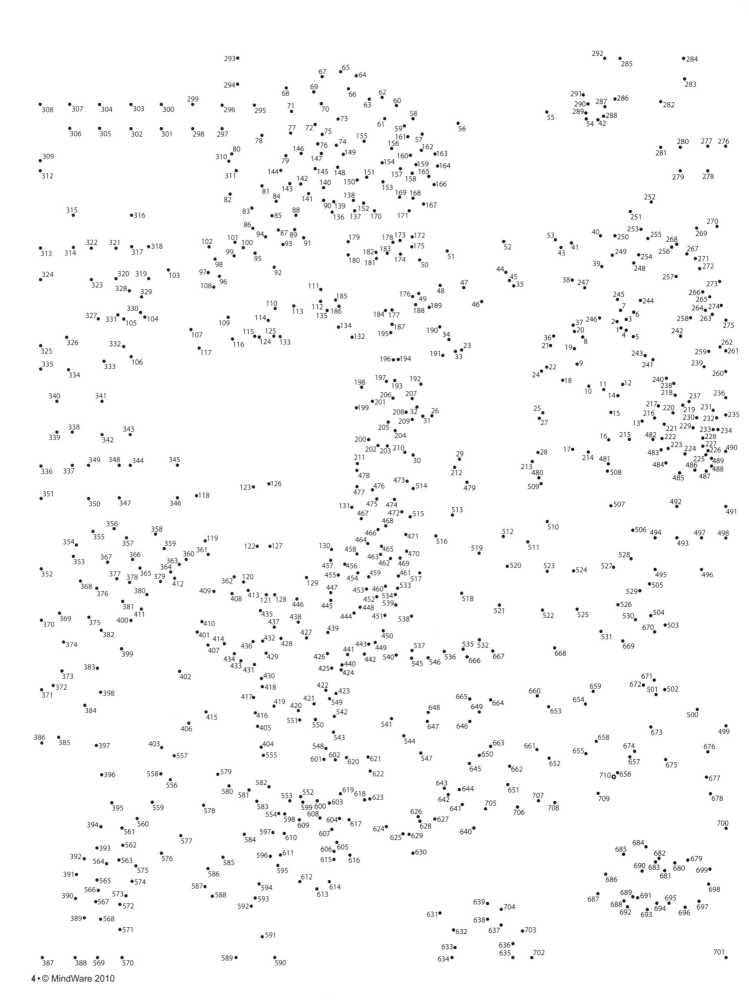

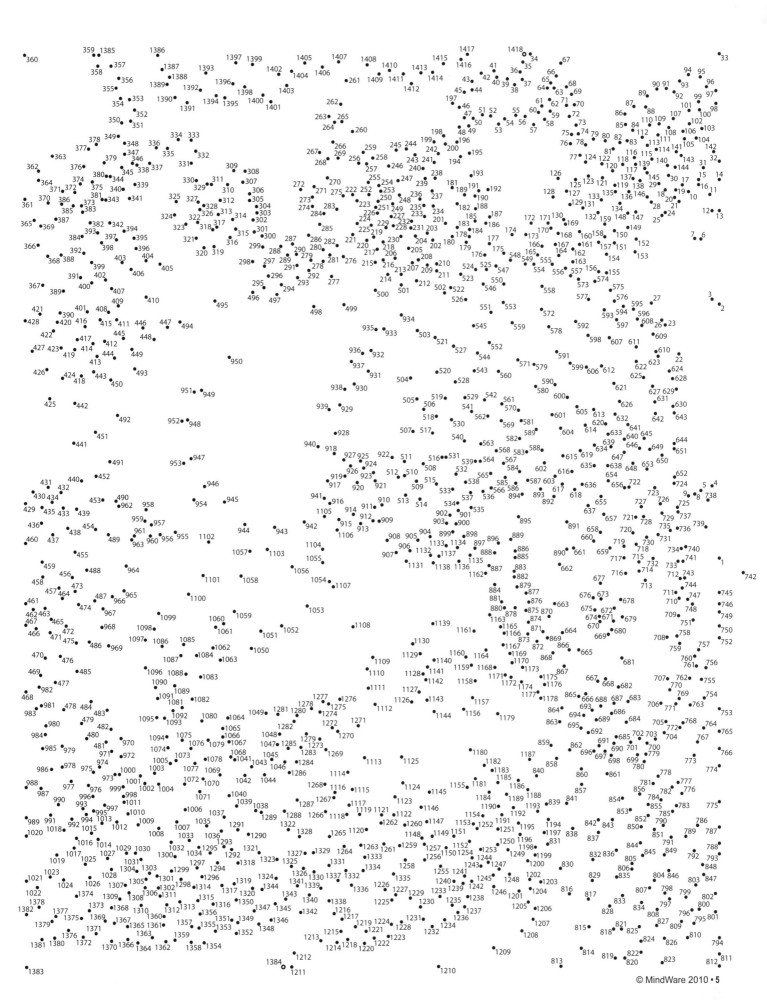

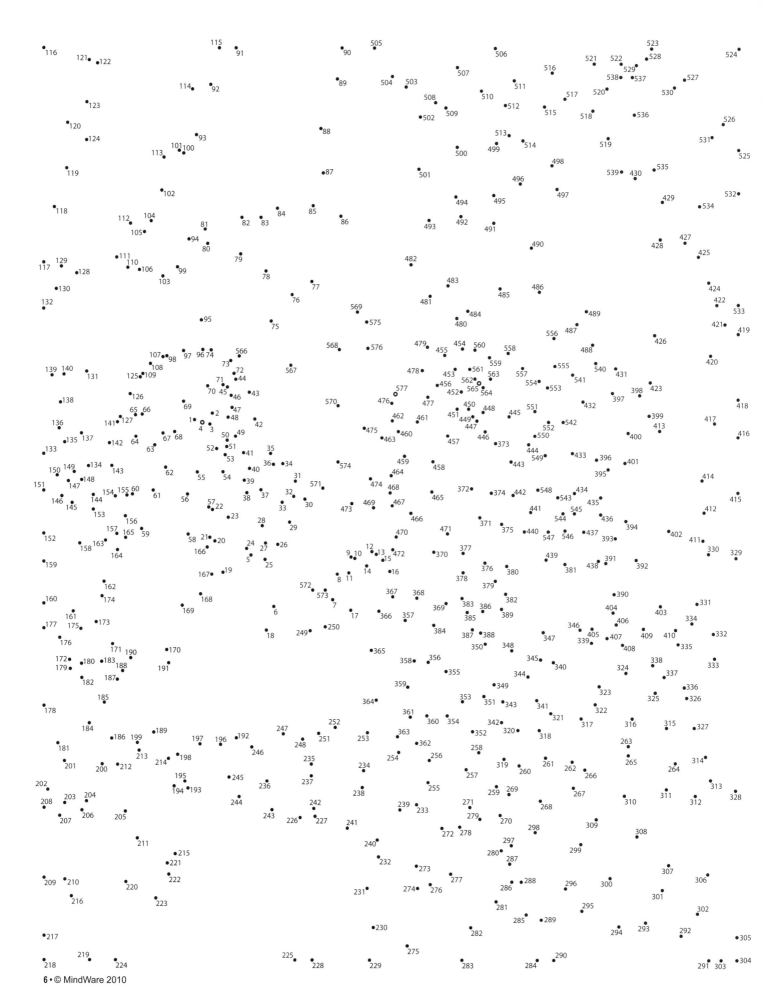

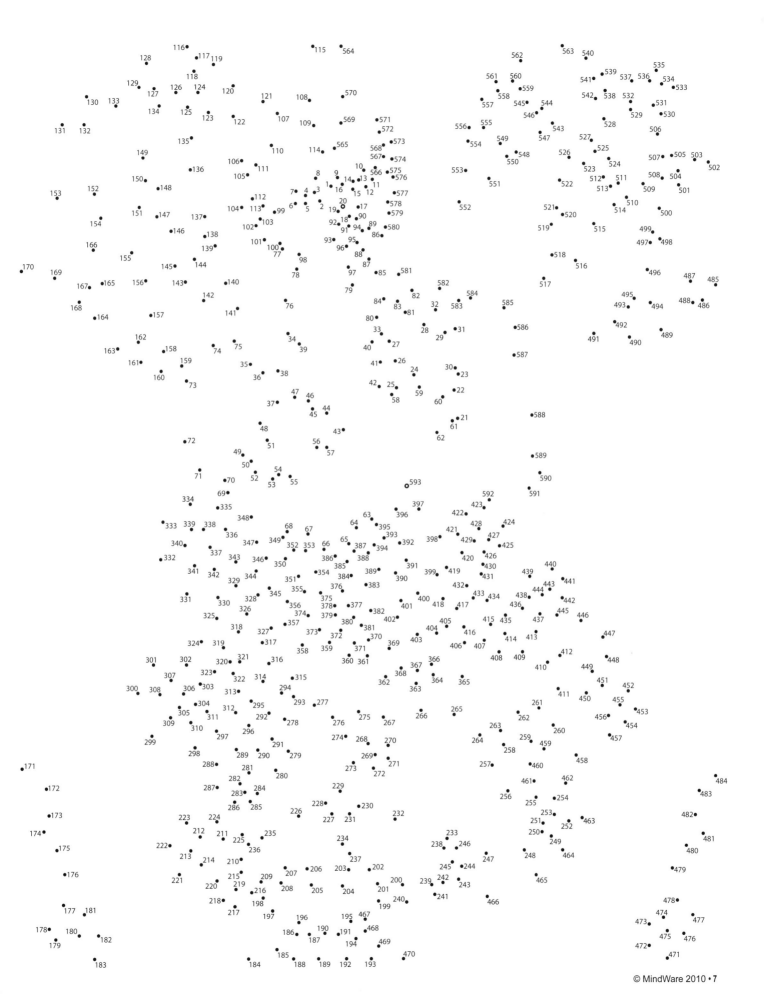

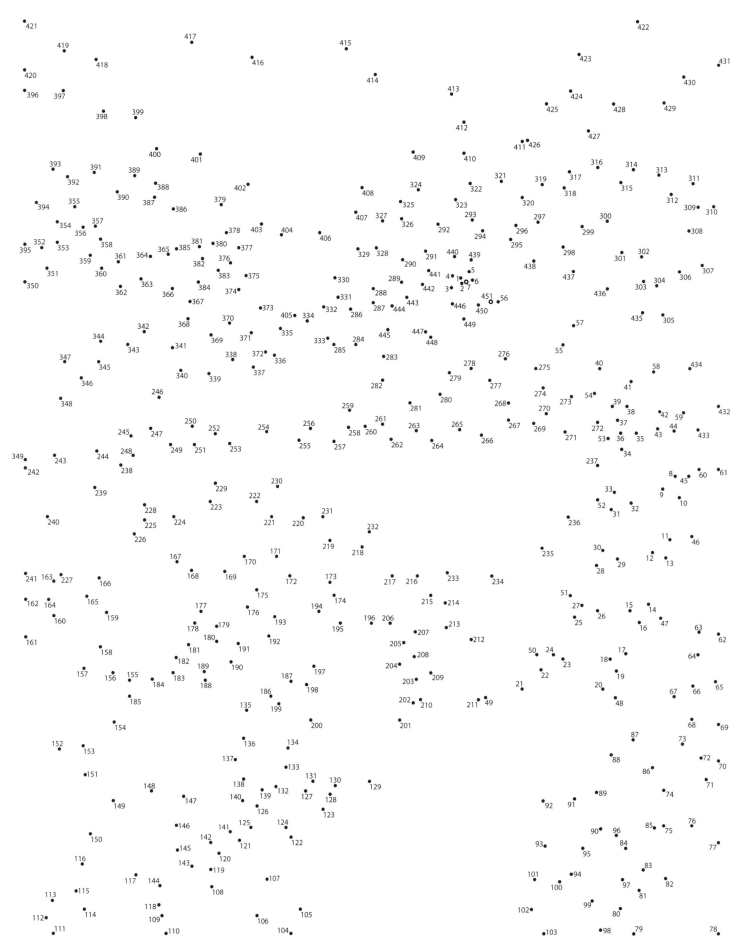

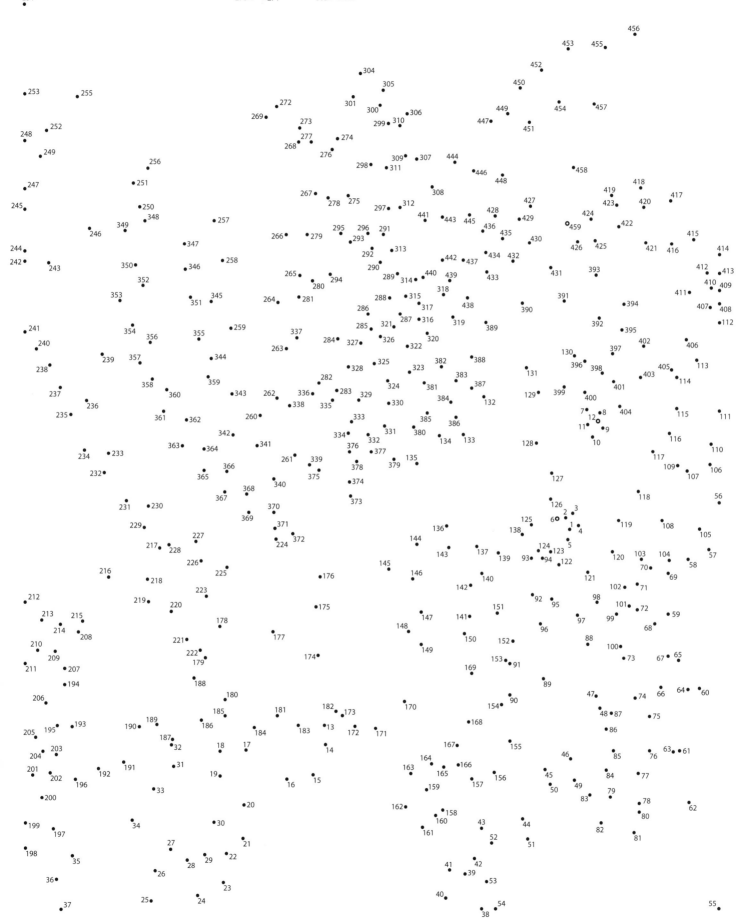

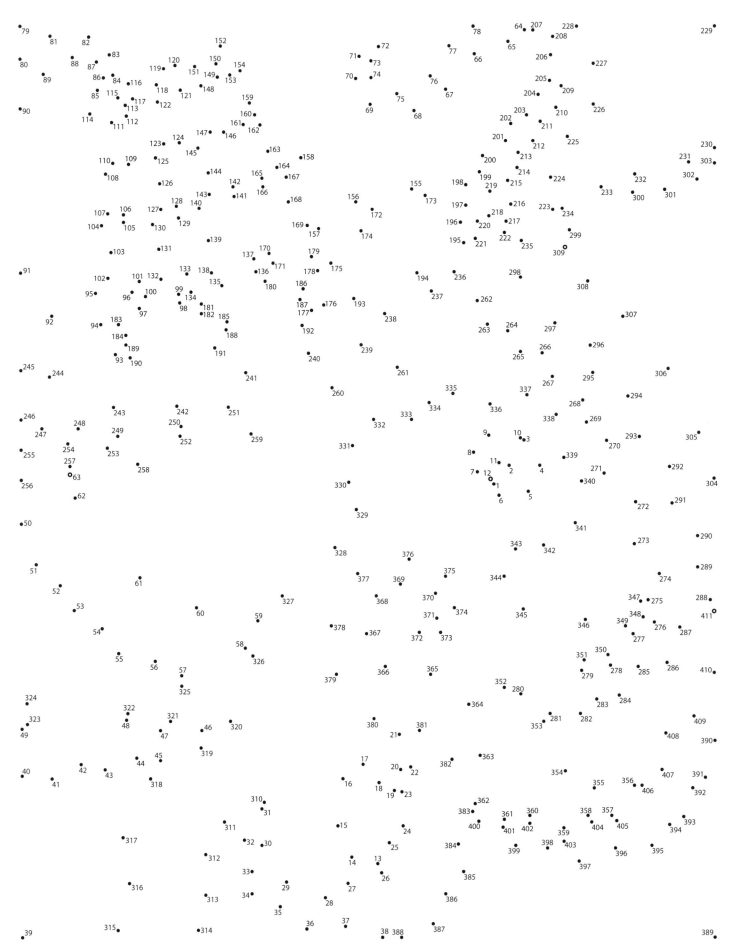

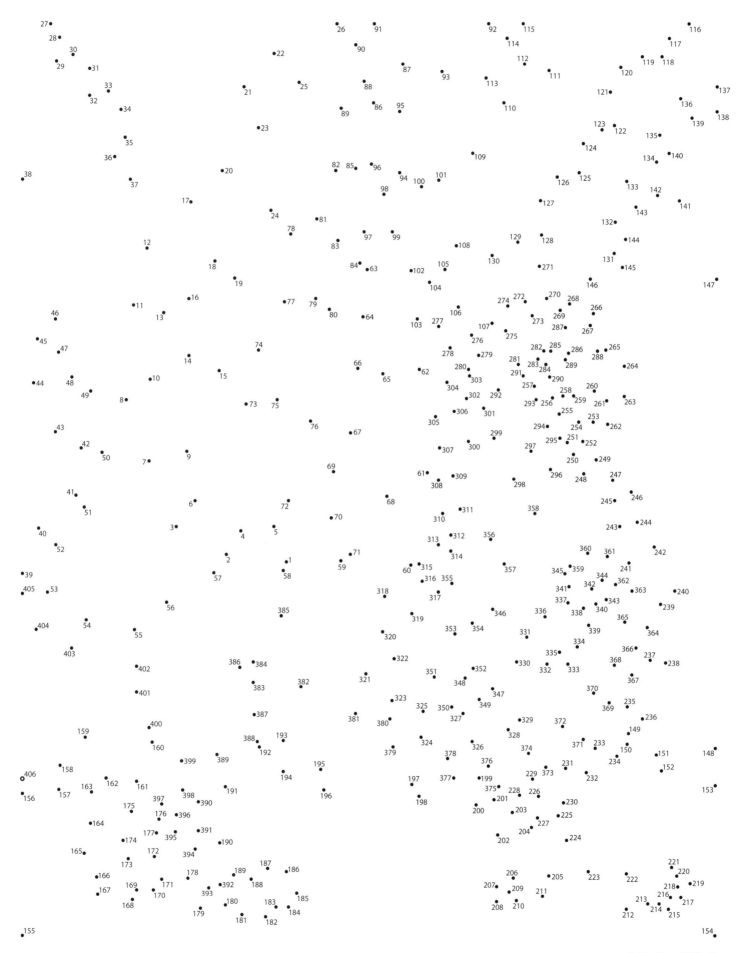

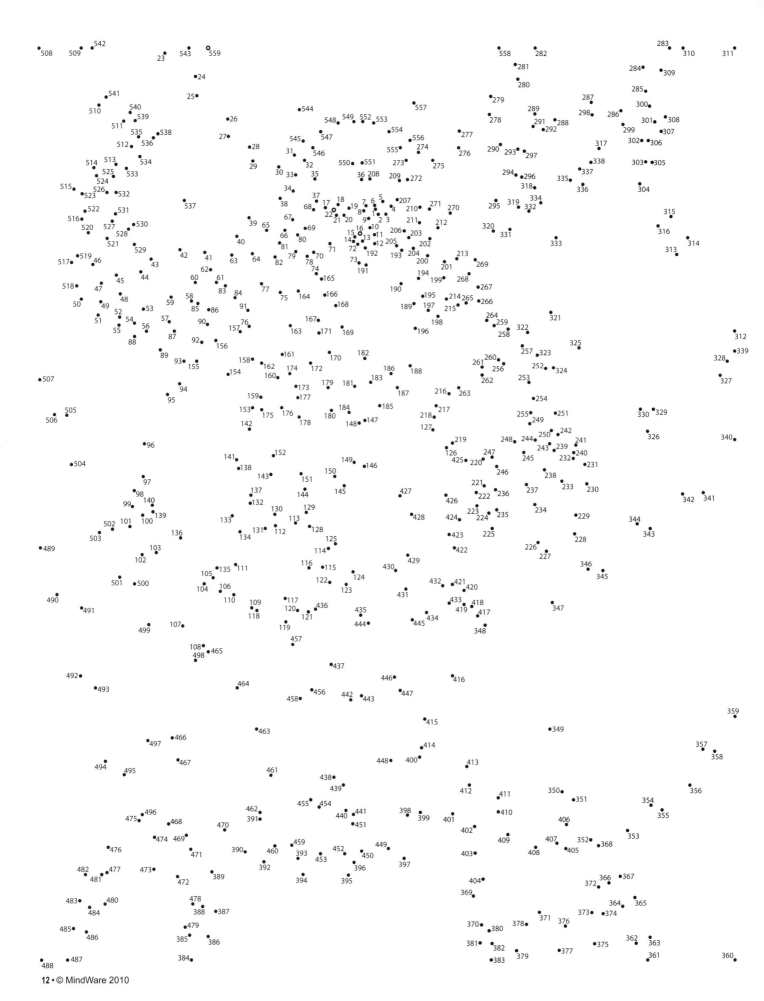

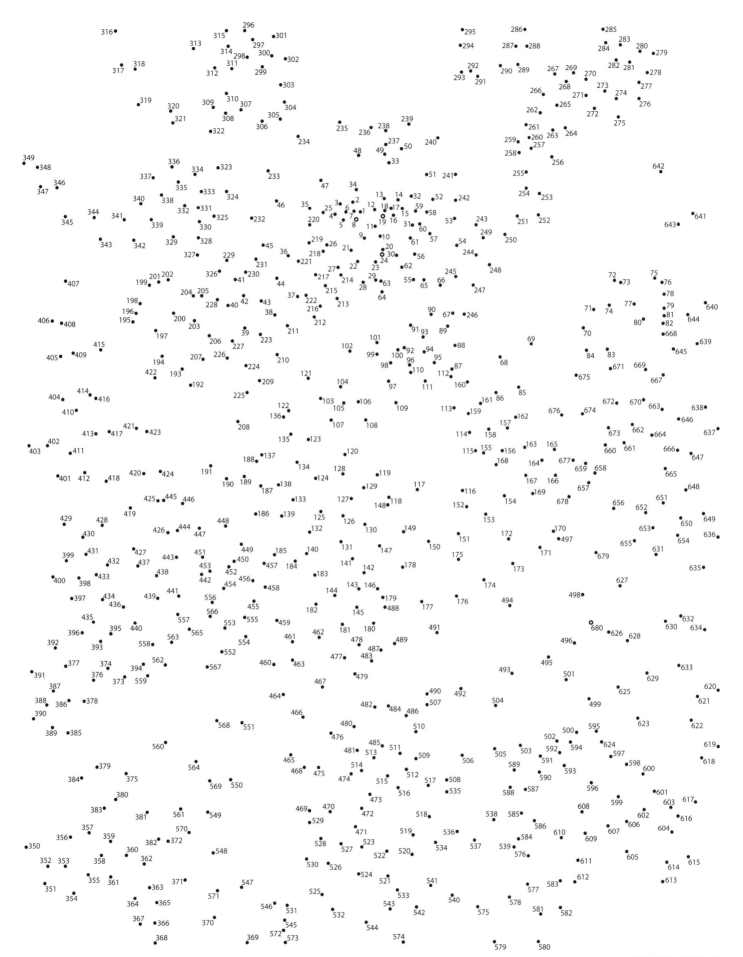

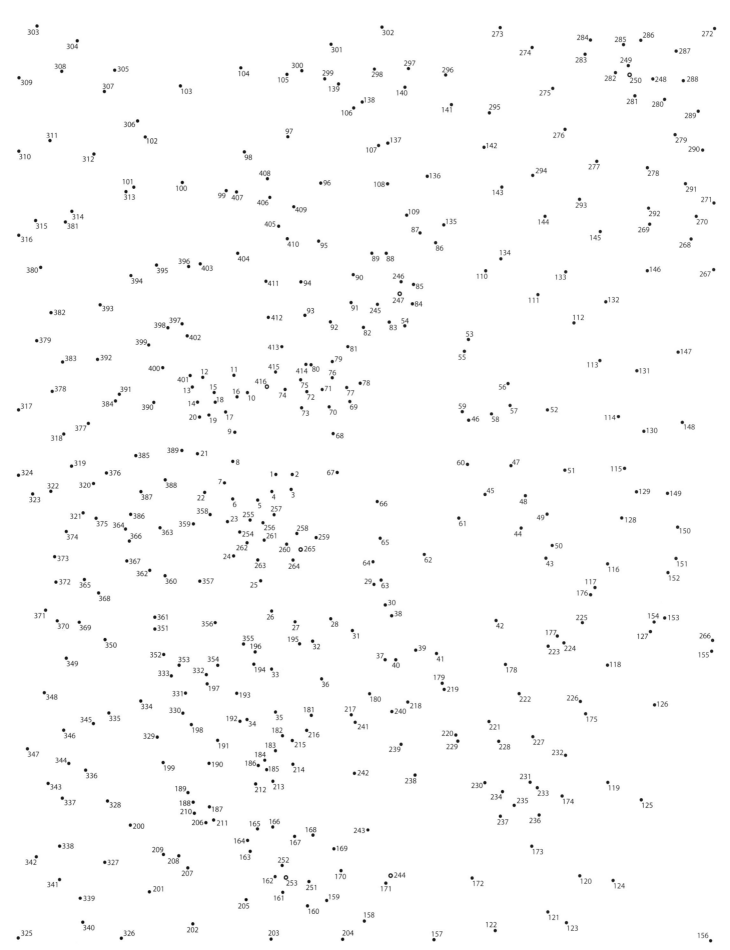

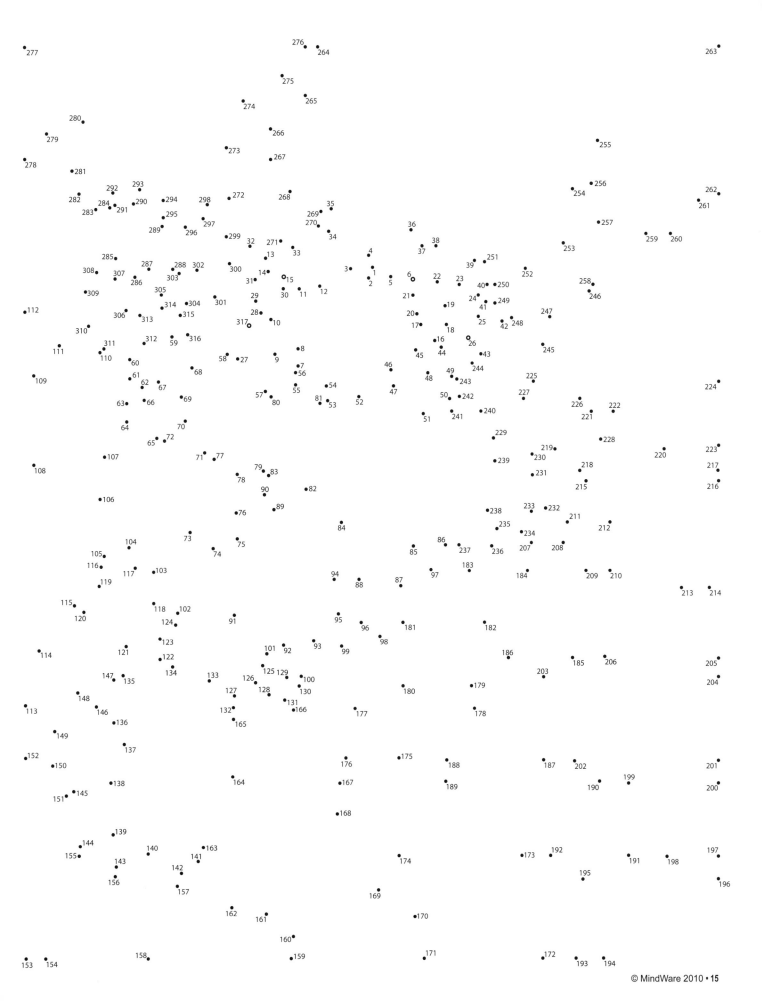

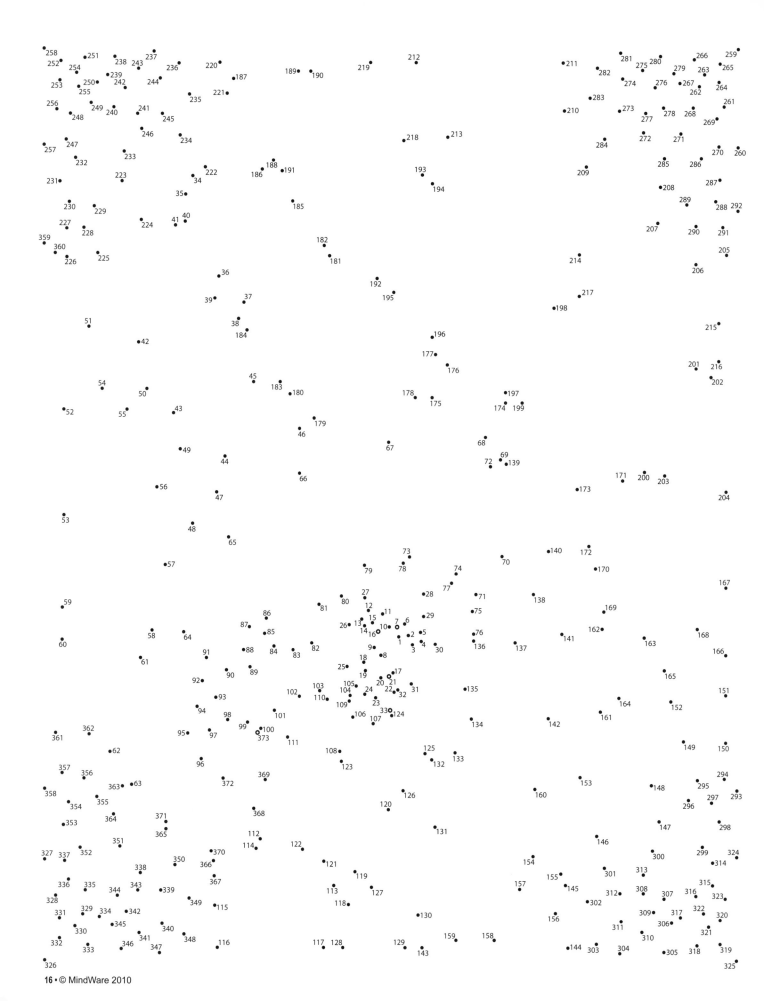

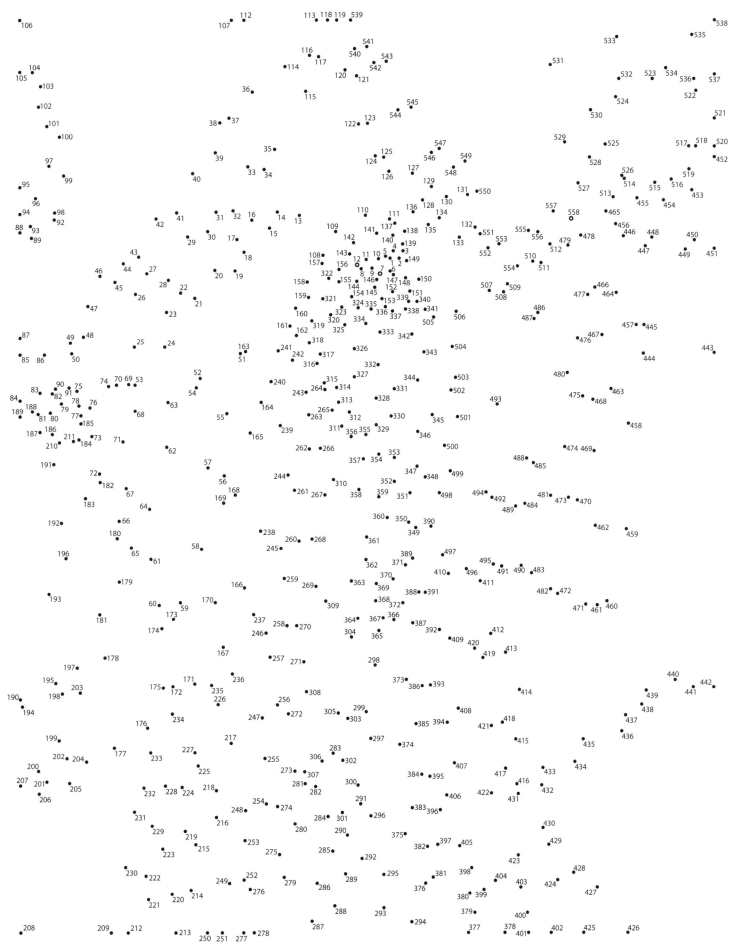

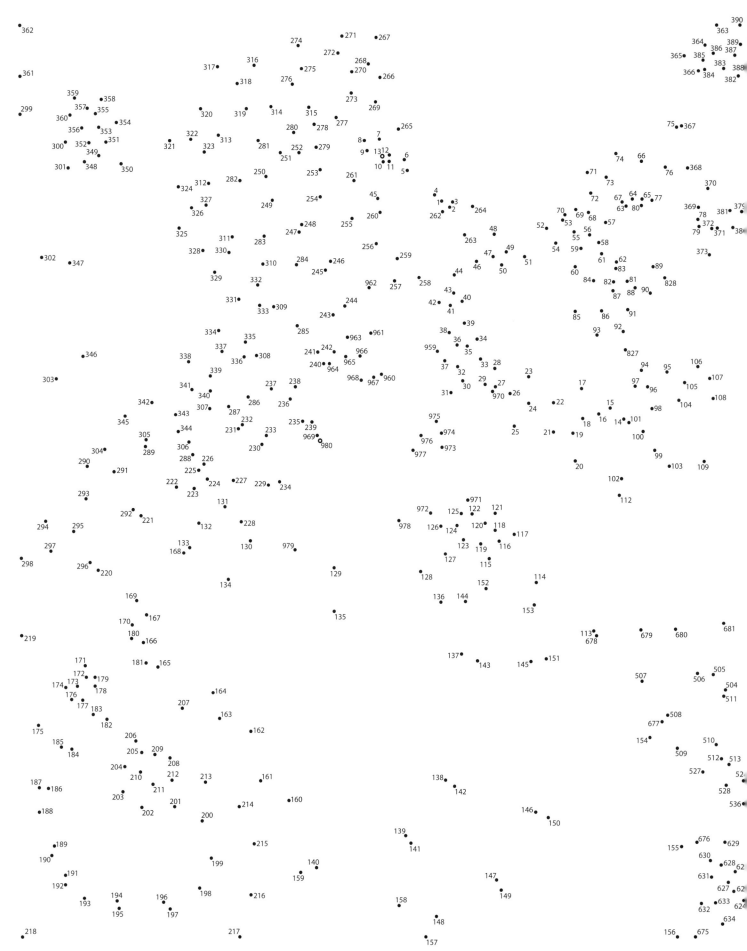

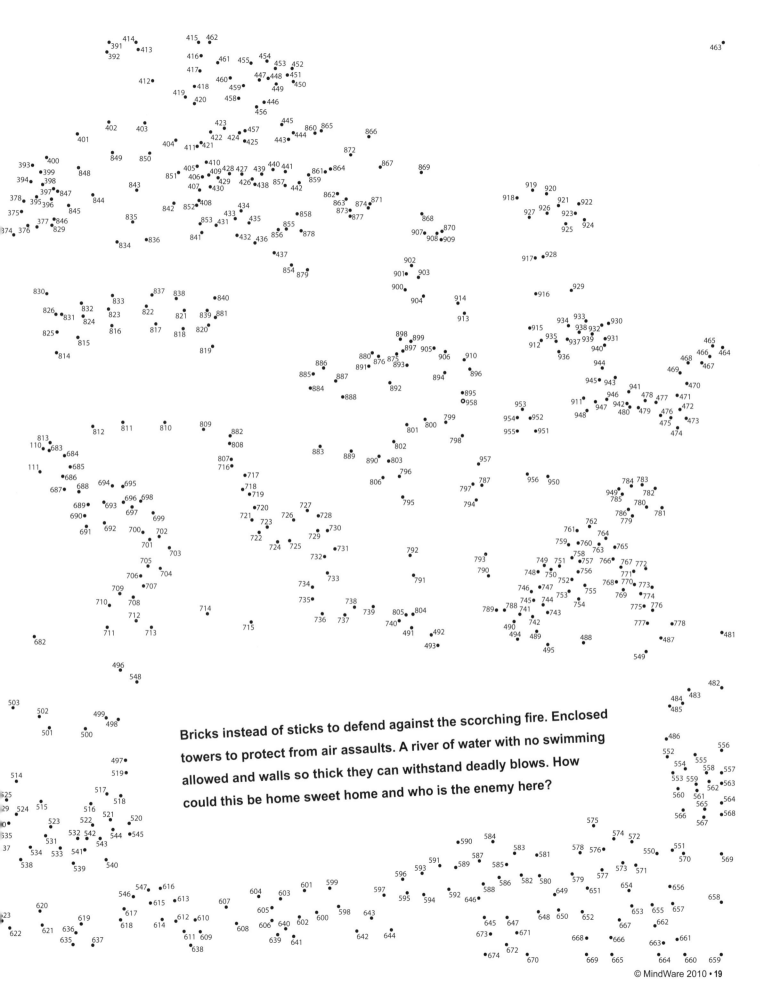

Bricks instead of sticks to defend against the scorching fire. Enclosed towers to protect from air assaults. A river of water with no swimming allowed and walls so thick they can withstand deadly blows. How could this be home sweet home and who is the enemy here?

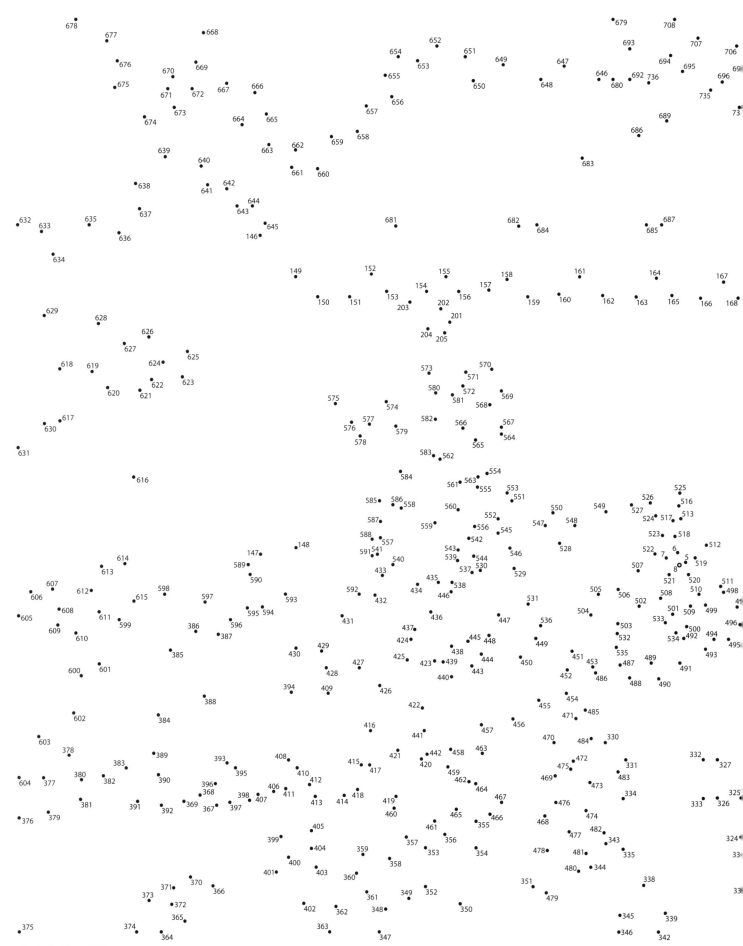

A boy named Perceval, raised apart from civilization, felt called to become a knight and traveled to King Arthur's court. Although not trained as a knight, Perceval discovered he had supernatural strength and skills in a dangerous martial game played by knights. Mounted on his horse and armed with a lance, Perceval was prepared to defend the honor of Queen Guinevere in this one-on-one battle.

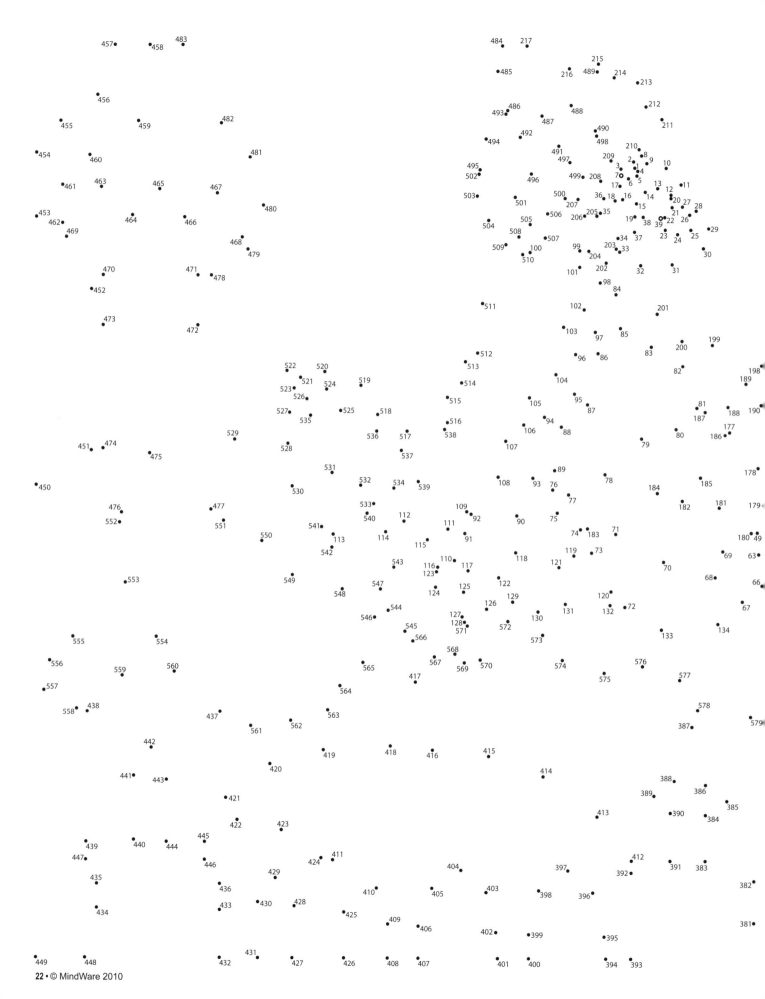

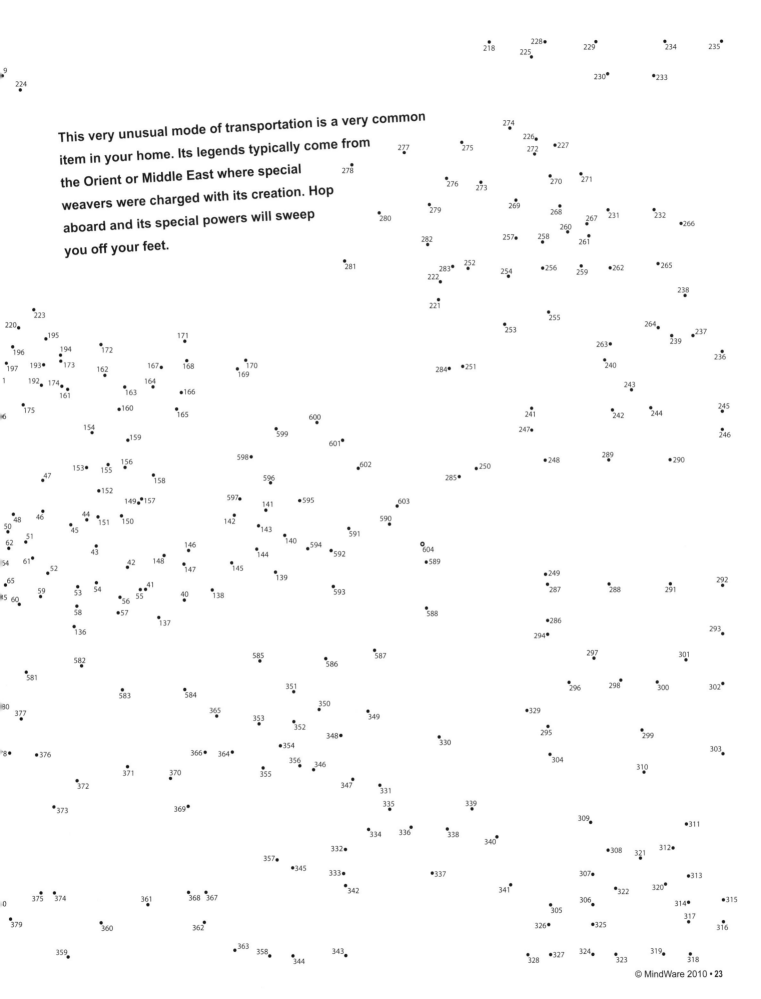

This very unusual mode of transportation is a very common item in your home. Its legends typically come from the Orient or Middle East where special weavers were charged with its creation. Hop aboard and its special powers will sweep you off your feet.

What has a horse head with a snake tail? Plus fish scales and eagle claws? This mythological creature is a mix of them all, with bat wings to boot! It is the only legendary animal of the Chinese zodiac. According to Chinese tradition, it has control over rain and floods, as well as the power to fly. Good fortune may be yours if your birthday lands within the date range governed by this animal.

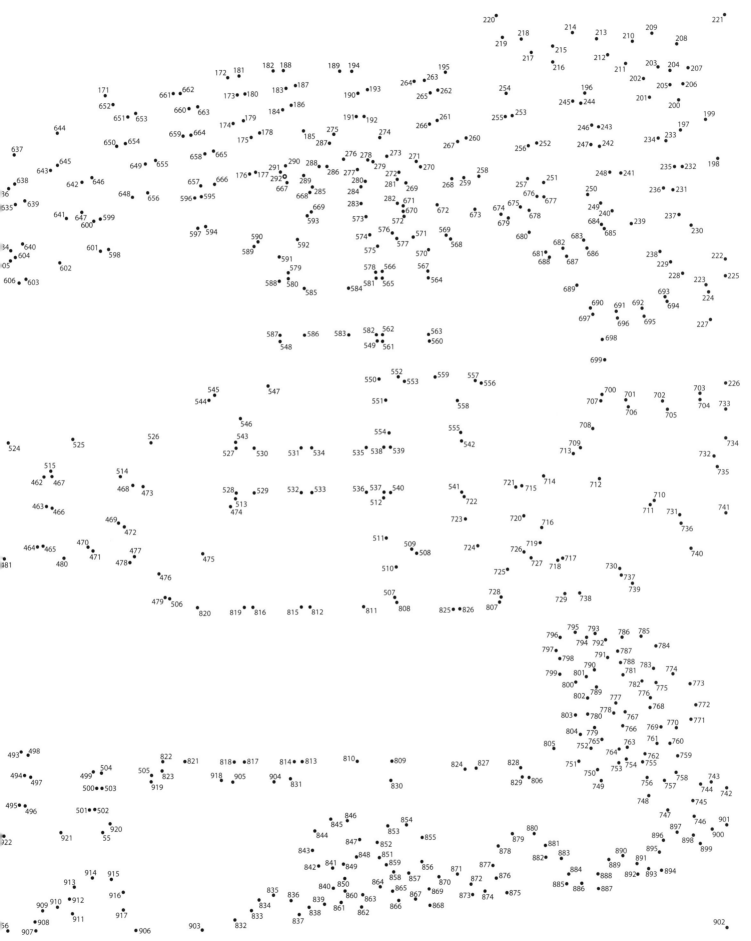

The ancient Greek philosopher, Plato, wrote of this island paradise. Was it a legitimate landform or a legend? It has been described as a great empire located in the Atlantic Ocean. The people lived here peacefully until they waged war and were defeated by the Athenians. Was it an earthquake or the god Poseidon that caused this city to sink to the ocean floor to be lost for all time?

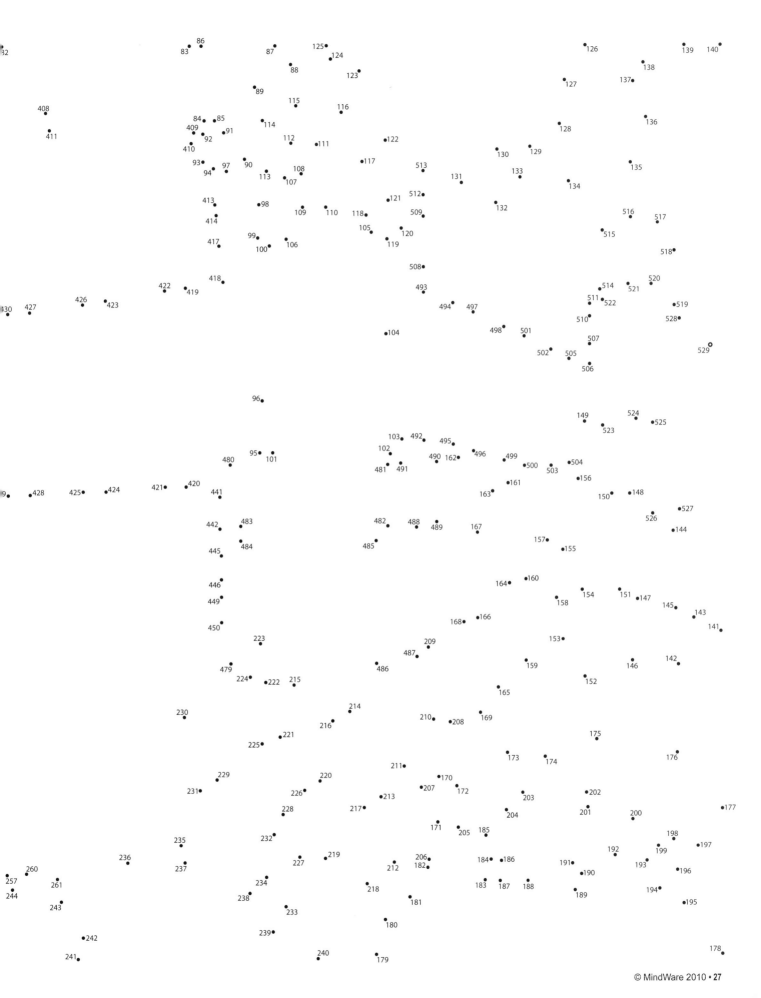

You are more likely to see a picture of this bearded god with a lightning bolt, scepter and eagle than in a loving family portrait. His father swallowed his siblings at birth, but this deity was protected by his crafty mother, who presented her husband with a swaddled stone. After growing up in hiding, he returned to overthrow his father and become supreme ruler of all gods. When he learned he would someday be dethroned by his own son, he swallowed his pregnant wife.

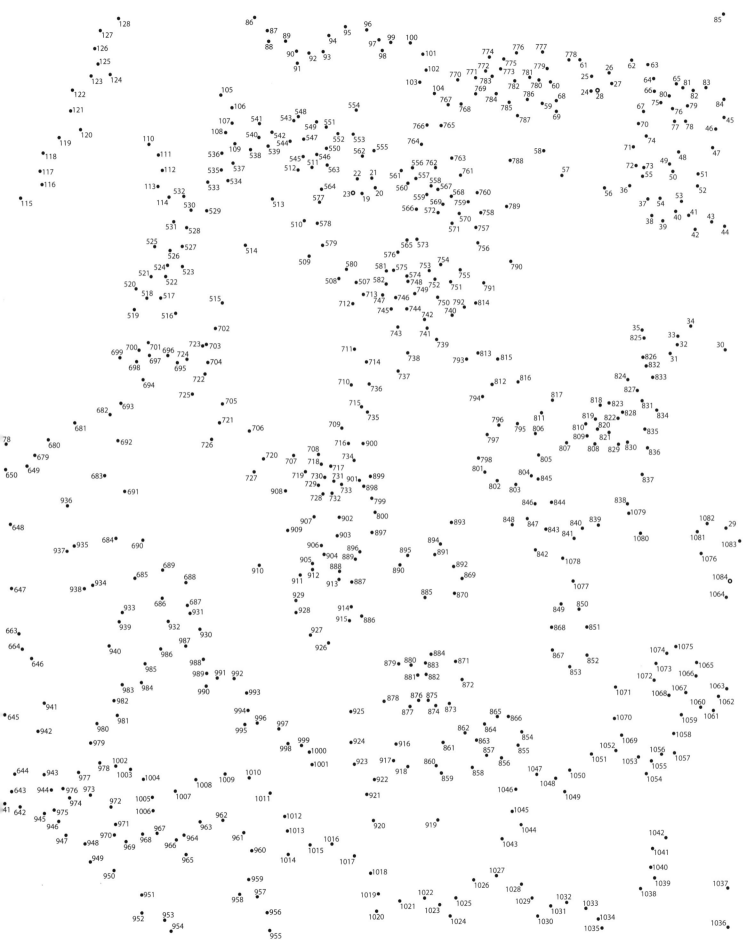

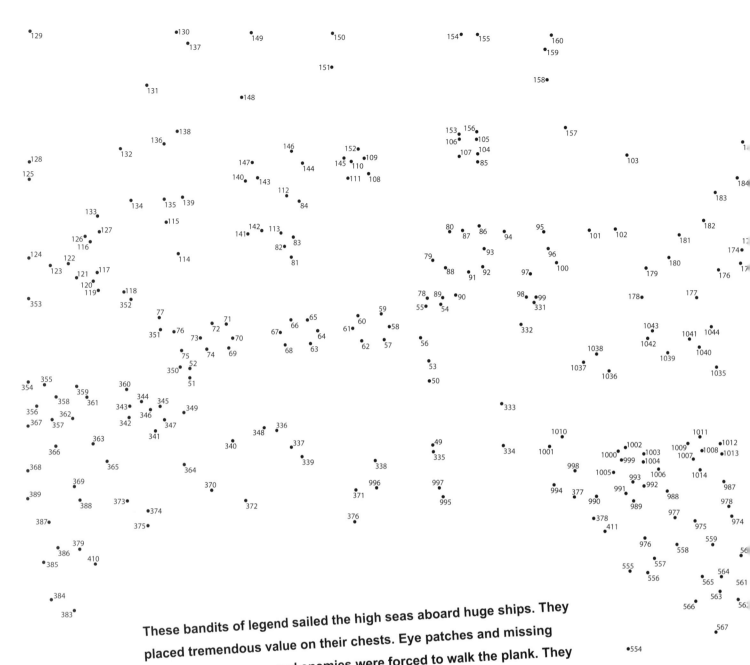

These bandits of legend sailed the high seas aboard huge ships. They placed tremendous value on their chests. Eye patches and missing limbs were common, and enemies were forced to walk the plank. They hoarded stolen valuables in secret locations. Will X mark the spot?

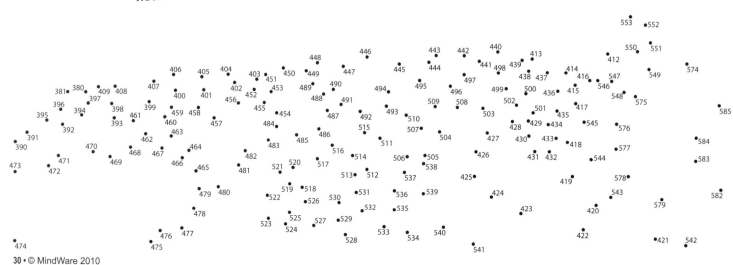

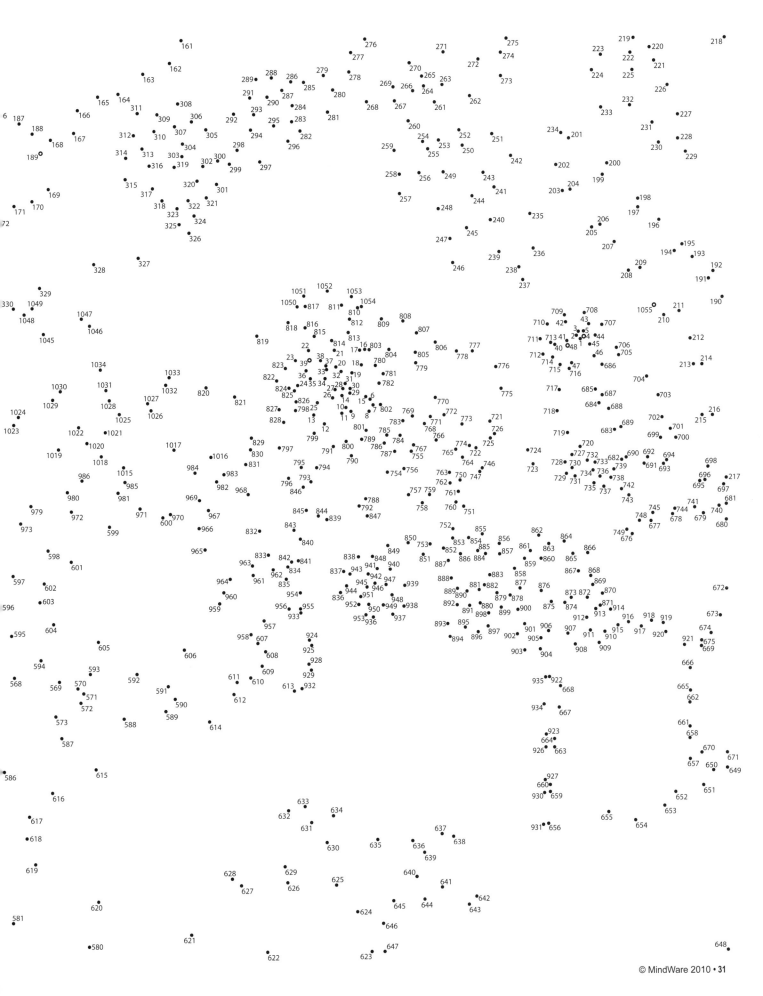

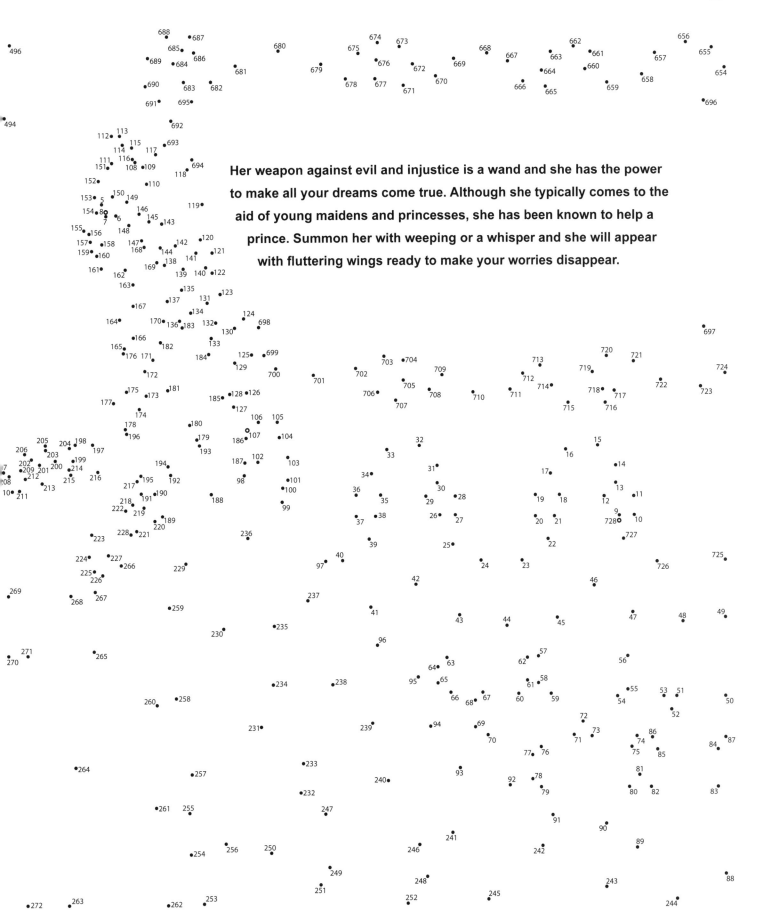

Her weapon against evil and injustice is a wand and she has the power to make all your dreams come true. Although she typically comes to the aid of young maidens and princesses, she has been known to help a prince. Summon her with weeping or a whisper and she will appear with fluttering wings ready to make your worries disappear.

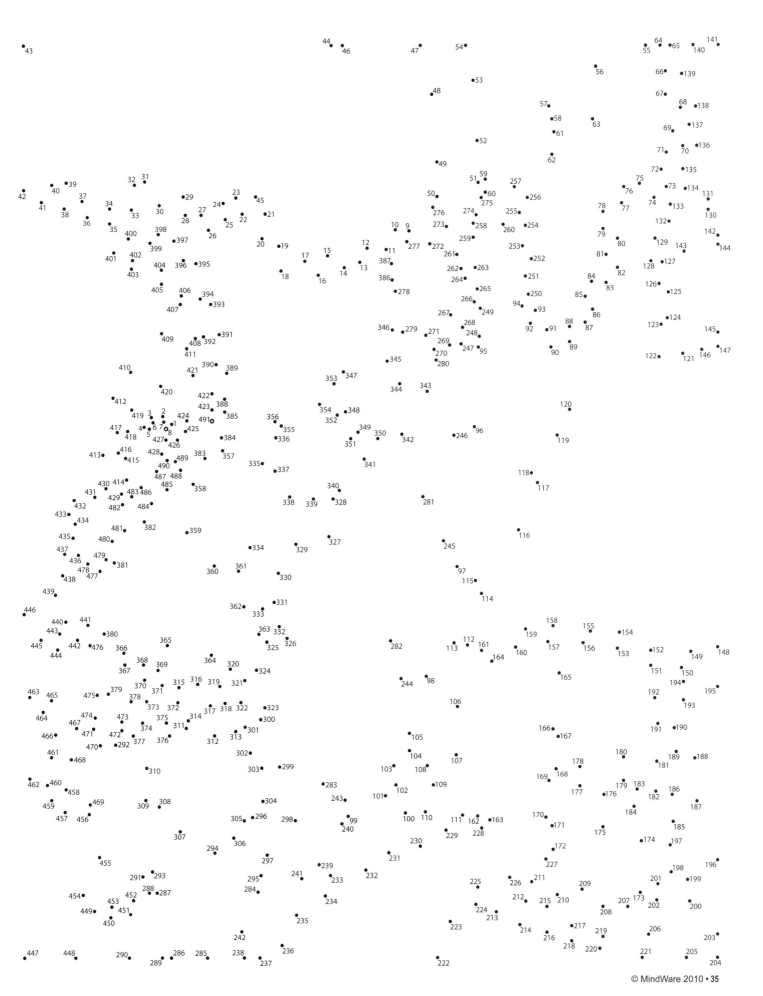

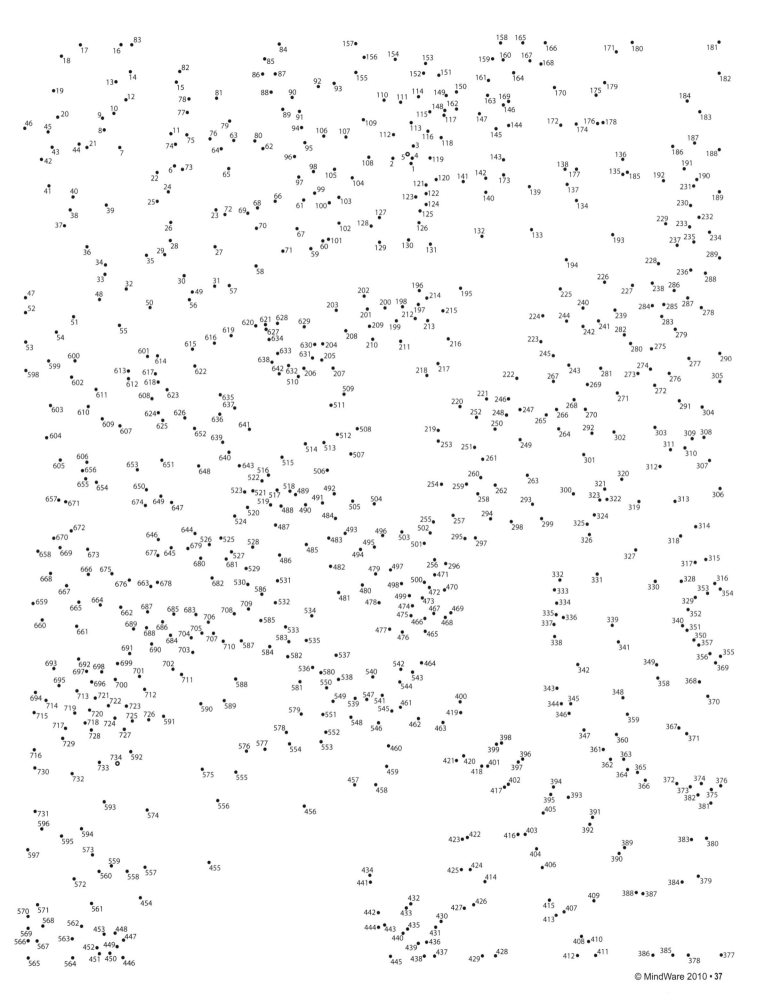

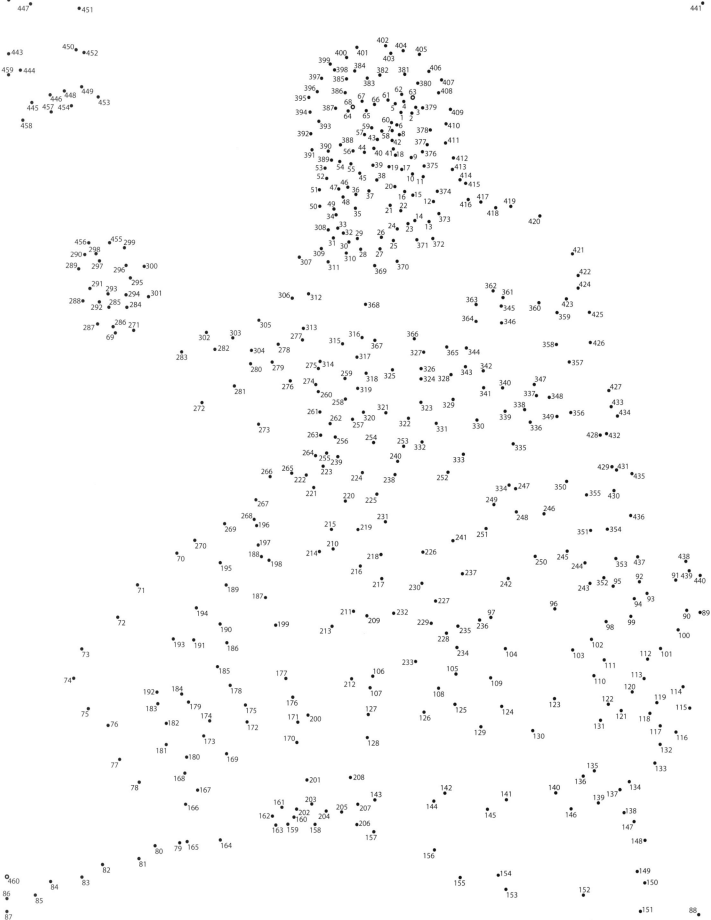

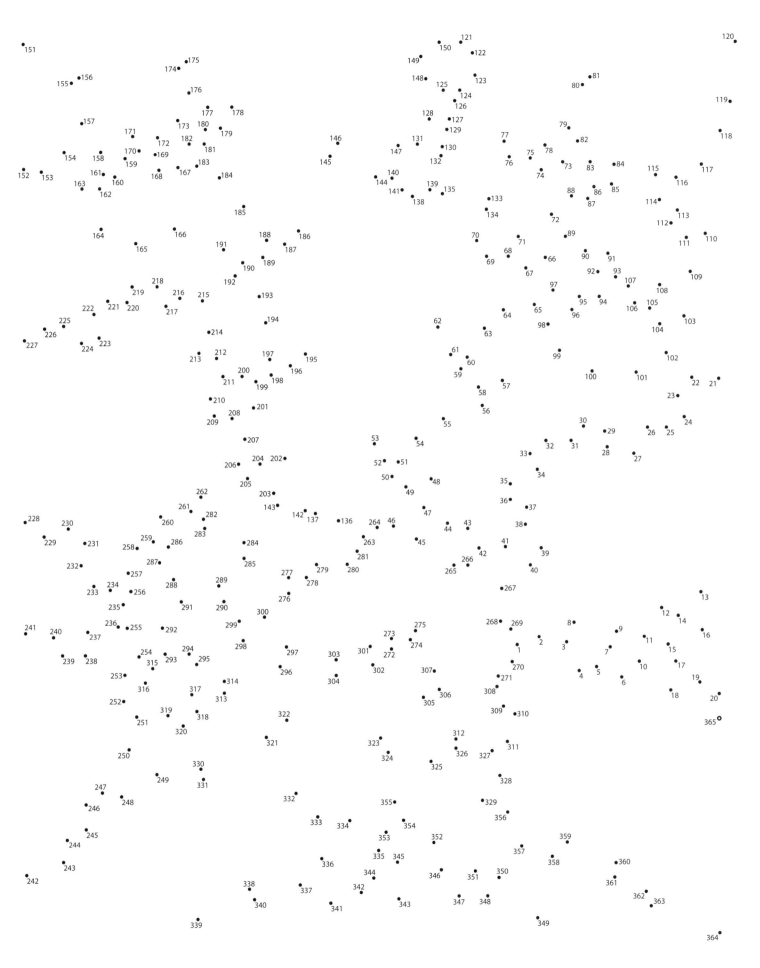

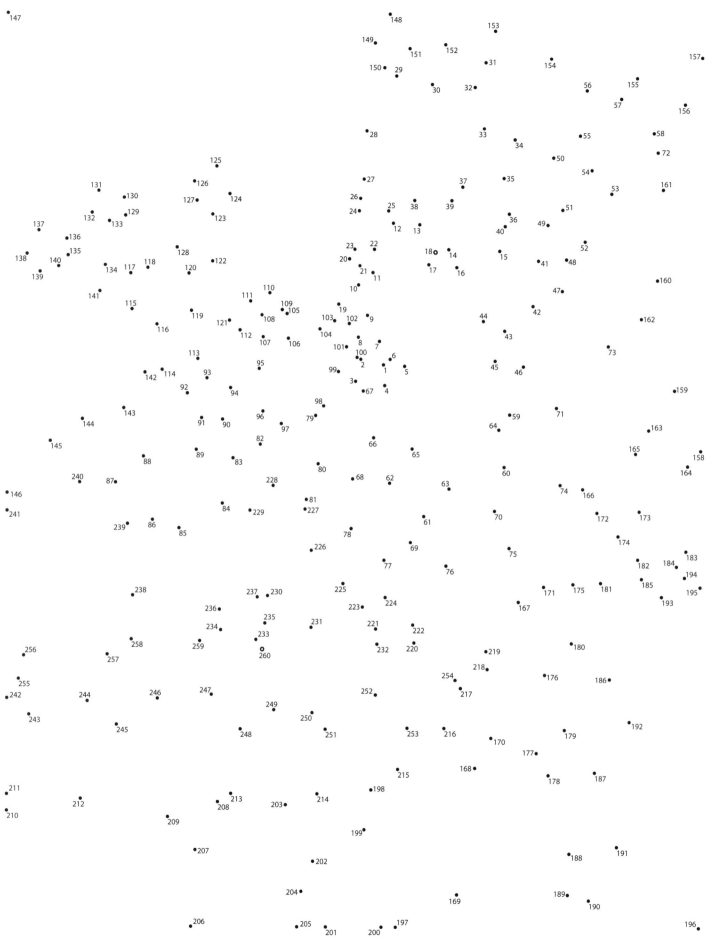

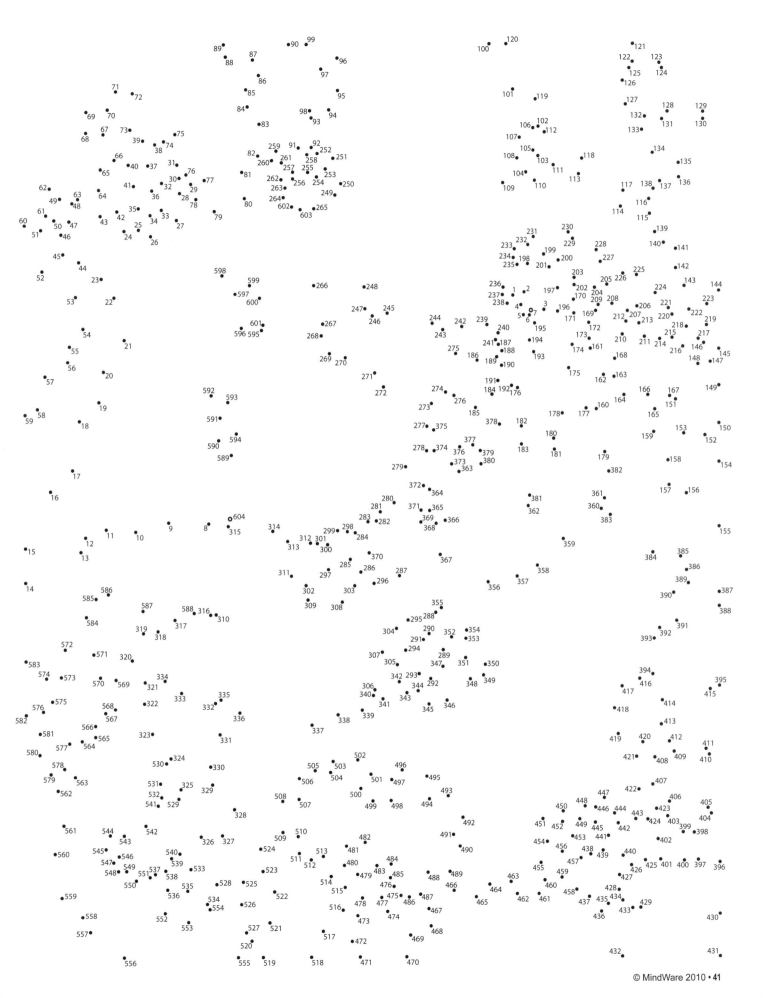

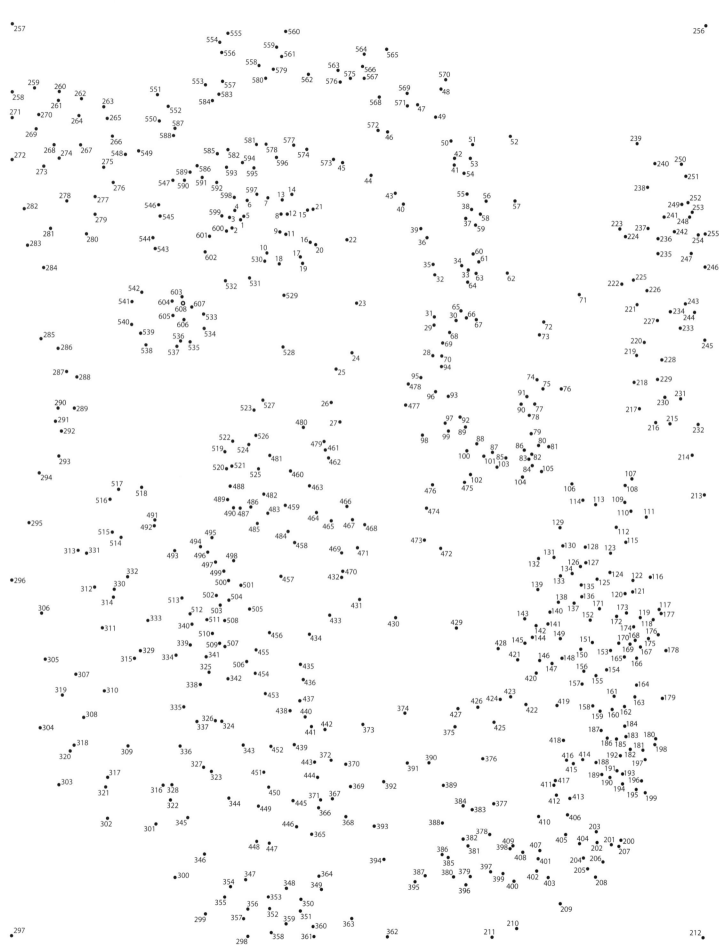

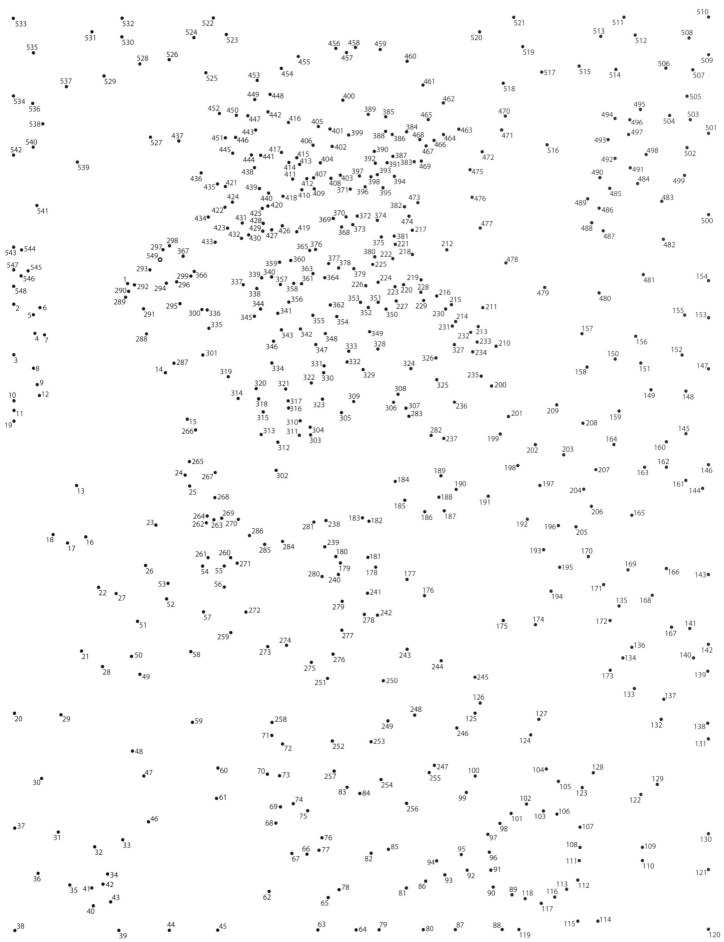

Solutions

Following are the images that result once each puzzle is completed. Be sure to color the final picture...you will be amazed at the transformation!

Page 4

Knight • 710 dots

A knight of the Middle Ages was sworn to uphold the values of faith, loyalty, courage and honor. A knight of legend fought dragons, guarded vast fortunes and protected sacred objects of unimaginable power.

Page 5

Fairy tales depict the unicorn as a beautiful and peaceful white horse with a single spiraled horn but legend also tells of black unicorns with exceptional speed, powerful, war-ready unicorns with golden horns, and brightly colored unicorns that foretold the birth of emperors.

Unicorn • 1,384 dots

Page 6

Although fairies are believed to exist in many different forms, all fairies are also believed to share four common characteristics: magical powers, invisibility, human traits and ties to nature.

Fairies • 577 dots

Page 9

Pegasus is the famed winged horse of Greek mythology, created upon the death of Medusa and destined to remain a constellation in the Northern Hemisphere.

Pegasus • 459 dots

Page 7

Genie • 593 dots

With origins in Arabia, the genie was believed to be more than a human but less than an angel. Great magicians captured the genies and imprisoned them in brass oil lamps, urns and bottles to harness their magical powers.

Page 8

Loch Ness Monster • 451 dots

First reported by a Viking in 565 AD, the Loch Ness monster is believed to be a 30-foot creature that closely resembles the Plesiosaurus, a dinosaur thought to be extinct for 65 million years. Monster sightings still occur today and bring millions of dollars in tourist revenue to Scotland each year.

Page 10

Kraken are believed to be gargantuan octopus-like sea monsters measuring over 200 feet long that decades ago sank ships with their enormous tentacled arms. Some think kraken live today in hibernation in the depths of the Norwegian Sea.

Kraken • 411 dots

With the head and wings of an eagle and the body of a lion, the griffon was a fierce creature that built its nest from gold and devoured any man who tried to steal it.

Griffon • 406 dots

Thor • 559 dots

The Norse god of thunder, Thor was one of the most powerful, ferocious gods, serving as the protector of all against the forces of evil. His hammer had the power to throw bolts of lightning.

Since the early days of sea exploration sailors have reported sightings of mermaids—creatures with the upper body of a woman and the tail of a fish. Even Christopher Columbus recorded a mermaid sighting in his captain's log.

Mermaid • 680 dots

Once a beautiful mortal, Medusa was transformed by the goddess Athena into a creature with snakes for hair and a face so ugly that whoever looked at her eyes would turn into stone.

Medusa • 416 dots

The Minotaur was a bull-headed monster who lived in a labyrinth maze where he was offered a regular diet of maids and youth to satisfy his cannibalistic hunger.

Minotaur • 317 dots

Princess in Tower • 373 dots

Countless fairy tale princesses have been locked in towers to await rescue from a prince. At least one real princess, Princess Elizabeth, was imprisoned in the Tower of London in 1554 as punishment for her supposed plot to overthrow her sister, Queen Mary.

Wizards, or sorcerers, wielded great mystical powers and in medieval times were often the reason for a king's success or failure. Perhaps the most famous of wizards is Merlin—trusted advisor of King Arthur.

Wizard • 558 dots

Pages 18 & 19

With walls up to 30 feet thick, towers up to 100 feet high, moats for defense, and drawbridges for access, medieval castles were constructed to withstand attacks from advancing armies and deadly dragons.

Castle and Dragon • 980 dots

Pages 20 & 21

Jousting • 748 dots

Perceval proved that he could excel at such knightly skills as jousting—a tournament in which knights use lances as weapons as they try to unhorse each other.

Pages 22 & 23

Able to instantly transport people who sit upon it, a magic carpet is a legendary, mystical element often found within tales from the Orient.

Magic Carpet • 604 dots

Pages 24 & 25

Chinese Dragon • 979 dots

The Chinese dragon is a long, four-legged serpentine creature in mythology and folklore that serves as a symbol of power, strength and good luck.

Pages 26 & 27

Plato told the story of the city of Atlantis, the capital of a beautiful island with a golden temple at the center that sank into the sea after a terrible earthquake.

Atlantis • 529 dots

Zeus • 1,154 dots

Wielding a thunderbolt as his weapon, Zeus was the god of the sky and supreme ruler of the Olympian gods.

According to legend, pirates buried treasure on tropical islands around the world. After hundreds of expeditions, many of the largest and most famous stashes have never been discovered.

Pirates and Treasure Chest • 1,055 dots

Fairy Godmother • 728 dots

A fairy godmother is a loving, maternal fairy who uses her magical powers to grant wishes and right wrongs.

The Cyclops is a Greek mythological giant with a single eye in the middle of its forehead. These giants were blacksmiths and gave gifts to the gods—to Zeus they gave the thunderbolt, to Poseidon the trident, and to Hades the helmet of invisibility.

Cyclops • 523 dots

Robin Hood was a heroic outlaw in English folklore, known for robbing the rich and giving to the poor with the assistance of his fellow bandits known as his "Merry Men."

Robin Hood • 491 dots

According to the German folk tale, when the Pied Piper played his magic pipe, he was able to attract all the rats in town with his music—luring them into the river.

Pied Piper • 573 dots

A fairy's personality can vary greatly—sometimes curious, often helpful and protective, occasionally mischievous and full of tricks.

Fairy • 734 dots

Poseidon • 460 dots

Poseidon is god and protector of the sea; his weapon is a trident that can shake the earth.

According to legend, a sword magically embedded in a stone could only be removed by someone worthy of becoming king. Many strong knights tried but it was a boy named Arthur who succeeded.

Excalibur • 365 dots

In most fairy tales, it takes a kiss to turn a frog into a prince. However, original tales required a night on the princess' pillow or a jolt against a brick wall!

Girl Kissing Frog • 260 dots

Hippocamp • 608 dots

The hippocamp is a mythological animal that is part horse and part fish, and is responsible for pulling the chariot of Poseidon, god of the sea.

The elf is a divine being with magical powers, often depicted as a little person living underground in hills, wells or springs. An elf's distinctive pointed ears are said to be a reflection of the leaves around them.

Elf • 549 dots

Raised in the African jungle by a tribe of great apes, Tarzan is a fictional character who grows up to become a wild, heroic adventurer.

Tarzan • 604 dots